GREG ANDERSON

The Mozart Anthology

Five arrangements for two pianos and piano, four hands
based on music by WOLFGANG AMADEUS MOZART

AWKWARD FERMATA PRESS

Published by Awkward Fermata Press.
www.gregandersonpiano.com

ISBN-13: 978-0-9830625-2-3

CONTENTS

(with programmatic notes by Greg Anderson & Elizabeth Joy Roe)

> In "Der, welcher wandert diese Strasse voll Beschwerden" ("Whoever walks along this path so full of troubles"), the enlightenment-seeking protagonist Tamino is warned by guards of the trials he must overcome to attain his goal and reunite with his true love Pamina. This somber and contrapuntal work is arranged for two pianos in homage to Busoni's divine piano transcriptions of Bach's chorale preludes.

> The "Papageno!" fantasy is a mash-up of Papageno's arias from Mozart's psychedelic opera *Die Zauberflöte*. Papageno, "birdman" and resident clown of the proceedings, sings joyously at his eleventh-hour reunion with his true love Papagena. Throughout the fantasy, the lines between humor and menace, fantasy and reality, and the masculine and feminine blur into a coquettish game of musical twister for piano, four-hands.

> In *"Soave sia il vento"* ("May the wind be gentle"), a pair of sisters bid a bittersweet and heartfelt farewell to their lovers departing by sea. The aria features an exquisitely beautiful melody soaring over a fluid accompaniment suggesting currents of water and wind, arranged straightforwardly here for two pianos.

> The "Grande Scherzo" recasts the swirling events that close Act I of Mozart's *Così fan tutte* as a four-movement sonata for piano duet. The result: a furiously flirtatious dance over a single keyboard. After bidding their lovers farewell, a pair of sisters are mercilessly tempted and tricked by the same men (in disguise!) to hilarious and breathless effect. The finale begins when the men burst into the room and poison themselves, having been unsuccessful in their attempts to seduce the women. Soon thereafter, a bogus doctor arrives to revive the scheming men. Conscious but hallucinating, they request a kiss of the "goddesses" who stand before them. Although the sisters are tempted, they adamantly refuse the men's comical advances.

> In his beloved Rondo "Alla turca," Mozart appropriated a number of characteristics from Turkish military music—most notably a predilection noisemaking!—and thus conjured a titillating, exotic musical experience for the delighted audiences of his day. *Ragtime alla turca* was composed to help twenty-first century audiences reconnect with the wild spirit of the original. By further appropriating international styles (including Turkish military music, the Viennese waltz, and American ragtime), this funkified version diverts considerably from the notes of Mozart's rondo, but still captures the utter joyousness and revelry, as well as the folksiness and virtuosity, of the original work.

Chorale Prelude

"Der, welcher wandert diese Strasse voll Beschwerden"
("Whomever walks along this path so full of troubles")
from *Die Zauberflöte*, K. 620

Arranged for two pianos by
GREG ANDERSON

Composed by
WOLFGANG AMADEUS MOZART

Papageno!

based on Papageno's arias in *Die Zauberflöte*, K. 620

Dedicated to Paul Hoffman

Concert fantasy for piano, four-hands by
GREG ANDERSON

Music by
WOLFGANG AMADEUS MOZART

16

"Soave sia il vento"

("May the wind be gentle")

from *Così fan tutte*, K. 588

Arranged for two pianos by
GREG ANDERSON

Composed by
WOLFGANG AMADEUS MOZART

Grande Scherzo

based on the Finale to Act I of *Così fan tutte*, K. 588

Dedicated to Indhira Rojas

Concert suite for piano, four-hands by
GREG ANDERSON

Music by
WOLFGANG AMADEUS MOZART

I. Presto ♩ = 80

"Si mora, si, si mora" ("Let us die, yes, let us die")

II. Allegro ♩ = 144

"Eccovi il medico" ("Here's the doctor")

34
mf
p
mf
mf
p
mf
39
mp
f giacoso
p
p
f giacoso
45
3 3 3
mf espressivo

34

38

III. Andante ♩ = 63
"Dove son?" ("Where am I?")

IV. Molto Allegro ♩ = 144
"Dammi un bacio" ("Give me a kiss")

Ragtime alla turca

based on the *Rondo "Alla turca,"* K. 331 by Wolfgang Amadeus Mozart

Dedicated to Michael Hawley

Concert paraphrase for two pianos by
GREG ANDERSON

Grandioso ♩ = 66

poco a poco accel.

poco a poco accel.

Tempo I

CPSIA information can be obtained
at www.ICGtesting.com
Printed in the USA
FSHW010242270120
66348FS